STORIES FROM
Mexico

Folklore of the World

Each of the Folklore of the World Books contains carefully selected myths and folktales most representative of a single country. These books will help children to understand people in other lands and will help them to develop an appreciation for their customs and culture. Peace for the world can come only through the spreading of this understanding and appreciation.

The Folklore Books are the third step in the Dolch program, *Steps to a Lifetime Reading Habit*. The series on these graded steps, starting with the most elementary, are: the First Reading Books, the Basic Vocabulary Books, the Folklore of the World Books, and the Pleasure Reading Books.

Folklore Books are prepared under the direction of Edward W. Dolch, formerly Professor of Education, University of Illinois. In all the series, emphasis is placed on good storytelling and literary quality, as well as on simplicity of vocabulary.

Books in this series are (to date):

Stories from Alaska
Stories from Canada
Stories from France
Stories from Hawaii
Stories from India
Stories from Italy
Stories from Japan
Stories from Mexico
Stories from Old China
Stories from Old Egypt
Stories from Old Russia
Stories from Spain

STORIES FROM

Mexico

Folklore of the World

by EDWARD W. DOLCH
and MARGUERITE P. DOLCH

illustrated by
ERNEST DE SOTO

GARRARD PUBLISHING COMPANY
CHAMPAIGN, ILLINOIS

Foreword

There are many volumes on the folklore of Mexico. Most of them intend to give a complete survey of Mexican folk tales of all kinds and to give each tale in as complete detail as it is told by the native storytellers. We should go to those volumes for a complete understanding of the folklore of Mexico.

For American children there is needed, however, a sampling of the most interesting and most characteristic of Mexican tales, told in a simple but interesting way. For this purpose, we present the *Stories from Mexico*.

These stories are told almost entirely in the "Storyteller's Vocabulary," which contains the 684 words most used in the telling of stories, as found by research. This volume is one of the "Folklore of the World," which forms one of the four "Steps to a Lifetime Reading Habit." (The First Reading Books, The Basic Vocabulary Books, The Folklore of the World, and The Pleasure Reading Books.)

As the peoples of the world come into ever closer and closer relationship, it is most important that Americans have full sympathy with, and understanding for all nations. One of the important ways of understanding any nation is to know its folklore. For in its folklore, every people have embodied much of their culture and wisdom.

E. W. DOLCH

Santa Barbara, California, 1960

Contents

Stupid Little Salvador

Salvador was the littlest burro. He lived in the country at the hacienda.

The hacienda was very beautiful. There were trees around the big house where the people lived. There were pretty red and yellow flowers.

At night, Salvador liked to hear the music that came from the big house. The other burros always went to sleep as soon as they ate the corn and the grass that Miguel gave them for their supper. But

Salvador tried to stay awake so that he could hear the music.

Every morning, Miguel took the burros into the town. First he tied a bundle of wood or a bundle of grass on the back of each burro. Carrying a load on his back was the work that each burro had to do.

Salvador liked to work. He liked to go to the town with a bundle of grass tied to his back. Miguel was careful to put only a small bundle of grass on Salvador's back. For Salvador was the littlest burro.

Sometimes the sun was very hot as Salvador walked along the road to town. But Salvador liked the hot sun. Sometimes the rain came down, and Miguel had to wear a poncho to keep dry. But Salvador liked the rain.

Salvador was a very happy little burro. But one day, when he was in town, he met George, the Goat.

"Do you live at the hacienda?" asked George, the Goat.

"Yes," said Salvador. "I live at the hacienda and it is a very beautiful place."

"I am sorry for you," said George, the Goat. "They say that burros have to work very hard at the hacienda carrying heavy loads on their backs. And they say that the burros are always hungry."

"Yes," said Salvador, "I carry a load on my back. And sometimes I am hungry. But when I get back to the hacienda, Miguel always gives me grass and corn. And at night, I like to hear the beautiful music from the big house. I like to live at the hacienda."

"I am sorry for you," said George, the Goat. "You think that you like to live at the hacienda because you do not know any better. They tell me that a hacienda is a very bad place."

By now Salvador was worried. He knew that he was the littlest burro. And the littlest burro did not know very much.

"Who tells you that the hacienda is a bad place to live?" asked Salvador.

"The animals that know told me about the hacienda," said George, the Goat. "They are the animals who go all over the world. The mosquitos, the flies, and the fleas told me that the hacienda is a very bad place."

And now Salvador was really worried.

"Oh, dear," said Salvador to himself, "I did not know that the hacienda was a bad place to live."

The Earthquake

When Miguel and the burros were going home, Salvador walked beside the Oldest Burro. The Oldest Burro was very wise, and knew everything.

"Grandmother," said Salvador, "do you like to live at the hacienda?"

"Sometimes when I am tired and the load of wood on my back is very heavy, I wish I could be a goat," said the Oldest Burro. "Then I would run away to the mountains and eat grass all day."

"Oh, dear," said Salvador to

himself. "Maybe George, the Goat, is right."

The Oldest Burro stopped to eat some grass by the road. Then she looked at Salvador and said,

"I have never lived any place but at the hacienda. And most of the time I am very happy there."

The next day, when Salvador was in town, he met George, the Goat, again.

"I am glad to see you," said George, the Goat. "I thought you had been killed."

"Why did you think that I had been killed?" asked Salvador.

"They told me that all the people and all the animals at the hacienda had been killed by an earthquake," said George, the Goat.

"Who told you that there had been an earthquake at the hacienda?" asked Salvador.

"The animals who go all over the world; the mosquitos, the flies and the fleas told me," said George, the Goat.

"I must be very stupid," said Salvador. "I slept all night. I did not know that there had been an earthquake at the hacienda."

Salvador was worried. He began to think that he was very, very stupid.

"This morning, the hacienda was just like it is every morning," said Salvador. "I ate my corn and grass. Miguel put the load of grass on my back. And then I walked down the long road to the town."

"You must be very stupid," said George, the Goat. "You don't see what is right before your eyes."

When Miguel and the burros were going home, Salvador walked beside the Oldest Burro.

"Grandmother," said Salvador, "do you see what is in front of your eyes?"

But the Oldest Burro was very tired and sleepy. She was walking along the road with her eyes closed. She did not want to talk.

When Miguel and the burros got to the hacienda, Salvador looked around him. Everything looked just as it had always looked. There was the big house where the people lived. There were the green trees and the red and yellow flowers around the big house.

Salvador went and stood beside

the Oldest Burro, who was eating the corn and the grass that Miguel had given her.

"Grandmother," said Salvador, "George, the Goat, told me that there had been an earthquake at the hacienda. He told me that all the people at the hacienda had been killed. He told me that all the animals at the hacienda had been killed."

"George, the Goat, is very stupid," said the Oldest Burro. "He makes up stories so that he can feel important. There was no earthquake at the hacienda last night. Look at it. What do you see?"

Salvador was very happy. Everything at the hacienda was just as it had always been.

"I will not believe all the stories I hear," said Salvador. "I will believe what I see with my own eyes."

The Little Ant

Once there was a little Ant. She worked from morning until night. One day she found some money.

"What shall I buy with this money?" said the Ant to herself. "I could buy some candy. But then I would eat the candy and it would be all gone."

The Ant went on working as hard as ever cleaning her house.

"I could buy a new broom to clean my house," said the Ant to herself. "But the new broom would soon be no better than my old broom."

The Ant sat down in her little chair and thought.

"I know how I will spend this money," said the Ant to herself. "I shall buy myself a new dress and some pretty shoes and a hat with a feather on it."

And that is just what she did.

The little Ant put on her new clothes. She did not work any more that day. She sat in front of her house and looked at the world.

A Cat came by.

"My dear little Ant, how beautiful you look," said the Cat. "My dear little Ant, will you marry me?"

"How will you talk to me after

we are married?" asked the Ant.

"I will say, 'Mew, Mew,' " said the Cat.

"No! No!" said the little Ant. "You would frighten me."

The little Ant sat in front of her house and looked at the world.

Soon a Dog came by.

"My dear little Ant, how beautiful you look," said the Dog. "My dear little Ant, will you marry me?"

"How will you talk to me after we are married?" asked the Ant.

"I will say 'Bow Wow,' " said the Dog.

"No! No!" said the little Ant, "You would frighten me."

The little Ant sat in front of
her house and looked at the world.
Soon a Lamb came by.

"My dear little Ant, how beautiful you look," said the Lamb. "My
dear little Ant, will you marry me?"

"How will you talk to me after
we are married?" asked the Ant.

"I will say 'Baa, Baa,'" said the
Lamb.

"No! No!" said the little Ant.
"You would frighten me."

The little Ant sat in front of
her house and looked at the world.

Soon Mr. Rat came by. He was
dressed in his best clothes and he
looked very fine.

"My dear little Ant, how beautiful you look," said Mr. Rat. "My dear little Ant, will you marry me?"

"How will you talk to me after we are married?" asked the little Ant.

And Mr. Rat said in a sweet little voice,

" 'Ee-ee-ee.' That is how I will talk to you after we are married."

"I like the way you talk," said the little Ant. "I will marry you. You shall be my husband."

The little Ant was very happy. And Mr. Rat was a very good husband.

The Cu Bird

When God made the birds, he made them without feathers. He put the feathers on them afterwards.

He put blue feathers on the Blue Bird. He put black feathers on the Crow. He put red feathers on the Red Bird. On some birds like the Parrot he put green and red and yellow feathers. He put feathers on all the other birds. The birds were very beautiful.

The feathers were all used up. And the Cu bird had no feathers at all. The Cu bird did not mind. But the other birds thought that it was very bad to have one of the birds without feathers.

"What is to be done about the Cu bird?" asked the Owl. "What will the other animals think if one of the birds has no feathers?"

The birds talked together. They all wanted to know what was to be done about the Cu bird.

"Something must be done," said the Blue Bird.

"We must do something for that poor little bird without any feathers," said the Red Bird.

And the black Crow said, "Caw, Caw, Caw. What can we do?"

Then the Owl spoke again and all the birds listened.

"We could each give the Cu bird one of our feathers," said the Owl. "We would never miss one feather. And there would be enough feathers to cover the Cu bird."

"Yes," said the Blue Bird. "That will be a good thing to do." And the Blue Bird began to pull out one of his pretty blue feathers.

"No! No! No!" cried the Peafowl, and she made so much noise that all the other birds listened. "If we

all give the Cu bird one of our
feathers, the Cu bird will be more
beautiful than any one of us. If
the Cu bird should look into the
fountain and see how beautiful he
looked, he would burst with
pride."

"The Cu bird must have
feathers," said the Owl. "I will look
after the Cu bird. And I am sure
that he will not burst with
pride."

Then each bird gave the Cu
bird one of its feathers. And the
Cu bird was the most beautiful
bird in the world.

The Cu bird walked up and

down so that the other birds could see his beautiful feathers.

The other birds were much pleased. But the Peafowl was not happy. She did not like the Cu bird to be the most beautiful bird in the world.

At last the Cu bird went to the fountain for a drink of water. He looked into the water.

"Oh! Oh! Oh!" cried the Cu bird. "I am the most beautiful bird in all the world."

Then the Cu bird flew up into the sky.

"I told you so. I told you so," cried the Peafowl. "The Cu bird will burst with pride. We will never see the Cu bird again."

The Owl had promised to look after the Cu bird and so the Owl flew up into the sky. But the Owl was such a big bird that he could not fly very fast. The Owl had to come back and sit in a tree.

The other birds were angry. They flew at the Owl. The Owl flew away and hid in a hole in the ground.

For three days and three nights the Owl hid in the hole in the ground. The Owl was getting very hungry and he did not know what to do.

Then the Owl heard something running around and around on the ground. He looked out of his hole, and saw the bird called the Roadrunner. So the Owl came out of his hole.

"Good morning, Señor Roadrunner," said the Owl. "I am very glad to see you. Will the other birds let me stay out of this hole in the ground?"

"Señor Owl," said the Roadrunner, "I am sorry to tell you that the other birds have said they are going to kill you. They think that the beautiful feathers made the Cu bird burst with pride."

"But I cannot stay in a hole in the ground," said the Owl. "I am very hungry."

The Roadrunner went away but very soon he was back with something good to eat for the Owl.

"Thank you, Señor Roadrunner," said the Owl. "But what am I to do? I cannot stay in this hole all of the time. I must go and find the Cu bird."

The Roadrunner thought for a long time and then he said,

"Señor Owl, you will have to hunt for the Cu bird at night when the other birds are asleep.

And I will hunt for the Cu bird in the day time.

That is why the Roadrunner runs up and down crying, "Cu-rut! Cu-rut! Cu-rut!," all day long.

And if you are out in the woods at night, you will hear the Owl crying, "Cu! Cu! Cu! Cu! Cu!"

But nobody has ever seen the Cu bird again.

The Sleepy Man

Once upon a time there was a Sleepy Man. He did not like to work. He liked to sleep.

Of course, the Sleepy Man did not have much money. Sometimes there was not much to eat in the little hut where he and his Wife lived.

Every morning the Wife would get up and open the door and the window and let the sunshine into the little hut.

The Wife would go and get some wood and make a fire. Then

she would make breakfast. Sometimes the Sleepy Man was so
sleepy that he would not even get
up to eat breakfast.

One morning there was nothing
in the little hut to cook for
breakfast.

"Wake up! Wake up!" said the
Wife to the Sleepy Man. "You
must go to your friend, the Storekeeper, and get us some food."

The Sleepy Man got up. He
rubbed his eyes. Then he went to
his friend, the Storekeeper.

"My friend, I wish some food,
for my Wife has nothing to cook

for my breakfast," said the Sleepy
Man.

"My friend," said the Storekeeper, "you owe me much money.
I do not want to give you any
more food until you pay me some
money."

"I do not have any money,"
said the Sleepy Man.

"If you do not have any money,"
said the Storekeeper, "I will let
you work for me. I have some big
stones that I want you to carry
away."

"Those stones are too heavy for
me to carry away," said the Sleepy

Man. "But do not worry about the money I owe you, my friend. To whom God wishes to give, He will give even if He has to put it in through the window."

The Storekeeper liked the Sleepy Man and so he gave him some food. The Sleepy Man went home to his Wife.

"Do not worry, my good Wife," said the Sleepy Man. "To whom God wishes to give, He will give even if He has to put it in through the window."

Then the Sleepy Man went to sleep again.

One morning, the Wife of the

Sleepy Man got up and opened the door and the window of the little hut. Then she went down to the spring to get some water.

But there was no water in the spring.

The Wife went back to the hut and said to the Sleepy Man,

"Wake up! Wake up! There is no water in the spring."

The Sleepy Man got up and went up the side of the mountain. He knew that he must find another spring, for his Wife had to have some water.

It was hard work going up the path on the mountain side. The

Sleepy Man stopped many times to rest. As he was sitting on a stone beside the path, he heard a horse running. The Sleepy Man looked up the path. He saw a fine Gentleman on a big horse. The horse was running away.

The Sleepy Man was not afraid of anything. He went out into the path and stopped the horse that was running away.

The Gentleman got down from his big horse and said to the Sleepy Man,

"Thank you for stopping my horse. I see that you are not afraid of anything. Come with me

and I will show you where a
treasure is hidden."

The Gentleman showed the
Sleepy Man a big pile of stones
beside the path. He pointed to
one stone.

"Lift that stone. You will find a
treasure under that stone," said
the Gentleman.

The Sleepy Man lifted the stone
to which the Gentleman had
pointed. He found a box under
the stone. When he opened the
box, it was filled with money.

But when the Sleepy Man looked
around, the Gentleman and the
big horse were gone.

The Sleepy Man tried to lift the box but it was very heavy. So the Sleepy Man put some of the money in his pockets. Then he covered the box with leaves and went home.

"My good Wife," said the Sleepy Man, "see what God has given to us." And he showed her the money.

The Sleepy Man told his Wife about the Gentleman on the big horse. He told her about the box of money that was on the mountain side under the leaves.

"Why didn't you bring the box of money home?" said the Wife.

"It was so heavy that I did not want to carry it," said the Sleepy Man.

"Some thief will get the money," said the Wife. And she began to cry.

"Do not cry, my good Wife," said the Sleepy Man. "Take this money and pay the Storekeeper the money I owe him. And buy us some good food. Remember, to whom God wishes to give, He will give even if He has to put it in through the window."

Then the Sleepy Man went to sleep.

In Through the Window

The Wife went to the Store-keeper. She gave him the money for the food he had given to the Sleepy Man.

The Storekeeper was very much surprised. He wanted to know where the Sleepy Man had gotten the money.

The Storekeeper went to the hut of the Sleepy Man. He found the Sleepy Man asleep.

"Wake up! Wake up! My friend,"

said the Storekeeper. "Tell me where you got the money."

The Sleepy Man opened his eyes.

"The Gentleman on the big horse showed me where the box of money was hidden under a stone," said the Sleepy Man.

"But where is the box of money now?" asked the Storekeeper.

"It is under a pile of leaves on the mountain side," said the Sleepy Man.

"I will go with my burro and bring the box home for you," said the Storekeeper.

"Thank you, my good friend," said the Sleepy Man. "I will give you half of all the money in the box.

"When I close my store this evening, I will get my burro and I will come for you. We will go up the mountain side together," said the Storekeeper.

The Storekeeper went back to his store. And the Sleepy Man went to sleep again.

The Wife sat in the door of the hut and waited for the Storekeeper. But the Storekeeper did not come. At last she said to the Sleepy Man,

"Wake up! Wake up! I think that the Storekeeper has gone up the mountain side to get the money for himself."

But the Sleepy Man only said, "To whom God wishes to give He will give even if He has to put it in through the window."

The Sleepy Man went to sleep again. And the Wife was so tired that she went to sleep too.

All day long the Storekeeper thought to himself, "Tonight I will go up the mountain side and find that box of money. The Sleepy Man was so lazy that he should not have the money. I will keep all of that money for myself."

When the Storekeeper closed his store, he called to his servant, "Go and get the burro."

The Storekeeper carried a light. He went slowly up the path on the mountain side. His servant and the burro walked behind. The Storekeeper looked carefully about.

At last the Storekeeper saw a pile of leaves beside the path. The servant found a box under the leaves.

The Storekeeper could hardly wait until he could see how much money was in the box. The servant opened the box. But there was nothing in the box but mud.

Now the Storekeeper did not know that this was magic treasure. Only the person to whom God had given the treasure could have it.

The Storekeeper was very angry. He thought that the Sleepy Man had played a joke upon him.

"I will play a joke on that Sleepy Man," said the Storekeeper.

He told his servant to put the box of mud on the back of the burro. The box of mud was heavy.

But at last the servant got it onto the back of the burro.

The Storekeeper took the box of mud to the hut of the Sleepy Man. Then he had the servant put the mud in the box against the door of the hut. He had the servant put the mud in the box against the window of the hut.

"Now, my good friend," said the Storekeeper. "I have played a joke upon you. The mud will get hard. You cannot open the door and you cannot open the window."

It was almost morning when the Storekeeper got home.

The sun was up when the Wife of the Sleepy Man woke. She went to the door to open it so that the sun could come into the little hut. She pushed and she pushed. But she could not open the door.

The Wife went to open the window so that the sun could come into the little hut. She pushed and she pushed. But she could not open the window.

"Wake up! Wake up!" said the Wife to the Sleepy Man. "I cannot open the door. I cannot open the window."

The Sleepy Man got up. He and his Wife pushed and pushed on the door. But they could not open the door. Then they pushed and pushed on the window.

At last the window opened just a little. In through the window fell a lot of money. The mud from the magic box had all turned to money again.

The Wife laughed and laughed as she picked up the money.

But the Sleepy Man just said, "I told you not to worry. To whom God wishes to give He will give even if He has to put it in through the window."

The Race

Long ago the Lord of the Woods called all the animals together.

"My dear children," said the Lord of the Woods, "I want to see how fast you can run. I want to have a race."

"Good! Good!" cried some of the animals. "Let us have a race from here to the big green tree that stands by the road."

"Yes," said the Lord of the Woods, "And to the one who wins the race, I will give the most beautiful sombrero in the world."

But not all the animals wanted to race.

"No! No!" said the Fox. "We cannot race with the Big Deer."

"No, No," said the Rabbit. "We cannot race with the Big Deer. No one can run as fast as he can."

Then a young Lizard came down from a tree.

"I will run the race," said the Lizard. "I will run the race against the Big Deer."

Then everybody began to laugh.

"Look at the Lizard," they cried. "His legs are so funny and short."

The animals laughed and laughed.

"You are all afraid to run a race with Big Deer," said the Lizard. "But I am not afraid. And I will wear the beautiful sombrero even if I have to wear it on my back."

The animals still laughed at the Lizard. But the Lord of the Woods said,

"Do not laugh at the Lizard. He is little, but he is not afraid."

The Lord of the Woods made a line across the road with a stick.

"Big Deer, come and stand on this line," said the Lord of the Woods. "And Little Lizard, come and stand beside Big Deer."

Now the race was to begin.
Little Lizard spoke.

"I must ask one thing," he said.

"What is it?" asked the Lord of
the Woods.

"I ask that all the animals close
their eyes when the race is to
start."

"All right," said the Lord of the
Woods. "Close your eyes, and I
will count to three."

When the animals opened their
eyes, all they could see was a
cloud of dust in the road. No
one could see Little Lizard. The
animals thought that he must be
buried in the dust.

The Lord of the Woods went straight through the air to the big green tree that stood beside the road. There was a bench under the tree. The Lord of the Woods sat on the bench.

Big Deer was running very fast. He was making a great cloud of dust. He said to himself,

"That poor little Lizard must be buried in the dust."

When Big Deer came to the bench under the big green tree, he found the Lord of the Woods waiting under the tree.

Big Deer started to sit down upon the bench.

"Oh, do not sit down on me," cried the little Lizard, who was sitting on the bench beside the Lord of the Woods. "I told you I would get here first, and here I am."

Big Deer was so surprised that he could not say a word.

Pretty soon, the other animals began to get to the big tree that stood beside the road. They all saw little Lizard sitting on the bench beside the Lord of the Woods.

"Little Lizard has won the race," said the Lord of the Woods. "And now I will give him the best sombrero in the world. But he is so small that I will have to put it on his back."

And ever after, the little Lizard has had beautiful red points along his back, which is the sombrero that the Lord of the Woods put there.

But the Lord of the Woods is the only one who knows that little Lizard won the race by hanging onto the tail of Big Deer. When Big Deer turned around to sit on the bench, little Lizard dropped off on the bench and sat there first.

The Young Lion

The first Lion in the world was getting very old. He knew that he was going to die. So he called his son to him and said,

"My son, I am going to die. You will have to take my place in the world. Remember, you are Master of all the animals. But let Man alone. He will hurt you."

"Is Man so big?" asked the young Lion.

"Man is small," said the first Lion in the world. "But Man can think."

When the first Lion in the world

had died, his son took his place.

"This is a very fine world," thought the young Lion to himself. "The animals in the world do just what I tell them to do. But I must find Man. I must make Man do just what I tell him to do."

The young Lion went off to find Man.

The first animal that the Lion met was the Snake.

"Is Man like you?" asked the Lion.

"Well," said the Snake, "Man is something like me. I can move very quickly. And Man can think very quickly."

The young Lion went on. The next animal that he met was the Eagle up in the tree.

"Is Man like you?" asked the Lion.

"Well," said the Eagle, "Man is something like me. I can fly very high. And Man's thoughts can fly very high."

The young Lion did not understand what the Eagle had told him about Man. He was very angry.

"I must find this Man," said the Lion to himself. "He shall not be Master of the World with his big thoughts."

Then the Lion met an Ox.

"Is Man like you?" asked the Lion.

"Well," said the Ox, "Man is something like me. I am very strong. And Man is strong in his mind."

The next animal that the Lion met was the Burro.

"Burro," said the Lion, "Do you know Man?"

"Yes," said the Burro. "I work for Man."

"Take me to Man," said the Lion.

"You had better leave Man alone," said the Burro. "Man is not very big but he can think."

The Lion was very angry.

"Take me to Man at once," said the Lion.

The Burro and the Lion went off toward the town where the Burro said that Man lived. On the way to town they met Coyote.

"Coyote," said the Lion, "are you anything like Man?"

"Yes," said Coyote. "Man is something like me. When the Moon is big in the sky Man likes to sing. I like to sing, too, when the Moon is big in the sky." And the Coyote laughed and laughed.

"What else does Man do?" asked the Lion.

"Man keeps chickens so that I will not get hungry," said the Coyote. And the Coyote laughed and laughed.

"Take me to Man at once," said the Lion. "I want to meet your good friend."

The Coyote started to run and the Lion followed him.

"There is Man," cried the Coyote. "He is riding on a horse."

The Lion ran toward the Man.

The Man saw the Lion coming. He turned and rode away. And the Lion ran after the Man.

The Lion ran so fast that he did not look where he was going.

The Lion fell into a big hole in the ground that the man had made to catch him.

The Man came and looked into the big hole.

"Do you want to fight with me?" asked the Man.

"Master of the World," said the Lion, "I cannot fight with you. Please help me out and I will go away and leave you alone."

The Man threw his rope around the Lion. Then Man and his horse pulled Lion out of the big hole.

The Lion went back to the animals. And after that the Lion left Man alone.

The Rabbit
in the Moon

Long ago the people of Mexico called themselves "The People Who Lived by the Rules." They thought that many gods lived in the sky. Sometimes the gods came to earth. And the gods gave the people the rules to live by.

Some of the gods were good. And some of the gods were bad. The bad gods sent the fire from the volcano. The bad gods sent the big winds that blew down the trees. One time the bad gods sent rain that covered the earth.

Long, long ago, the bad gods even killed the sun god. The sky was dark. The people of the earth could not see the sun in the sky. And the earth was dark and cold.

The other gods in the sky did not know what to do.

"We must have a new sun god," they said. "We cannot live in a dark sky. And the people of the earth cannot live on a dark and cold earth."

The gods in the sky talked together a long, long time.

One of the gods who was very

rich and powerful said, "I will throw myself into the fire. And the fire will make me the new sun god. Then I will be the most powerful god in the sky."

But there was another god who also wanted to do something big and fine. He said,

"The people on the earth cannot live if they have no sun. I will throw myself into the fire. And the fire will make me the sun god so that I can send light to the people of the earth and make them warm."

The gods in the sky made a big, big fire. First, the rich and powerful god ran to the fire. But he could not jump into the fire. Three times he ran to the fire but he could not jump into the fire.

Then the other god ran to the fire. He shut his eyes and jumped into the fire.

There was a bright light. When the gods looked at the sky, they saw a new sun god. And the new sun god was bigger and brighter than any sun god had ever been before.

The rich and powerful god was very sorry that he had not been the first one to jump into the fire.

Now he ran and jumped into the fire too.

There was a bright light. But it was not as bright a light as the light of the sun god.

When the gods looked at the sky, they saw the moon god. The gods in the sky were angry because they did not want a moon god. One of the gods threw a rabbit at the moon god.

The rabbit stuck to the moon. It never came back to earth again.

And that is why the children of Mexico think that they see a rabbit in the moon.

The Coyote and
the Sheep

One day a Fat Sheep and a Thin Sheep were walking down the road. They met Señor Coyote.

Señor Coyote was standing in the road looking at the sheep. And Fat Sheep and Thin Sheep knew what was on Coyote's mind.

"Don't eat me," said Fat Sheep. "I am so fat that I would make you sick."

"Don't eat me," said Thin Sheep. "I am so thin that you would find me nothing but bones."

Señor Coyote laughed and said,
"I am glad you spoke about something to eat, for I am very hungry."

"Eat the Thin Sheep first," cried the Fat Sheep.

"No! No!" said the Thin Sheep. "Eat the Fat Sheep first."

Señor Coyote thought to himself, "I am going to have some fun with these sheep before I eat them."

"Let us play a game," said the Coyote to the sheep. "Then I can tell which one of you I will eat first."

Señor Coyote drew a line across the road.

"Fat Sheep," said Señor Coyote, "You go thirty feet to the left of this line. Thin Sheep, you go thirty feet to the right of this line. When I say 'go,' run as fast as you can to this line. The first sheep that gets to the line will be the second one that I will eat."

The sheep did what the Coyote told them to do. They knew that if they tried to run away, Coyote would catch them.

"Are you ready?" called Señor Coyote and he was laughing to himself.

"Now 'go'! Run as fast as you can."

Señor Coyote stood on the line that he had drawn across the road. The sheep were running toward him. He thought that the sheep would run into each other when they came to the line across the road.

But the Fat Sheep and the Thin Sheep, as they ran, turned toward Señor Coyote. They hit the Coyote at the same time. The Coyote was tossed up into the air. All the breath was knocked out of him.

When Señor Coyote hit the ground he could not stand up. He

sat on the line in the middle of the road and wondered what had happened to him.

The Fat Sheep and the Thin Sheep ran away as fast as they could go. By the time the Coyote could stand upon his legs, the Sheep were far away.

Señor Coyote and Juan's Maguey

Juan was a country boy who lived in a little hut. He had one maguey plant. Juan was very proud of his maguey plant. For his maguey plant was the biggest plant on the country side.

All the people came to see Juan's big maguey plant. And Juan would always give them a drink of the sweet juice that came from the middle of the maguey.

One morning Juan went out to get the sweet juice from his maguey plant. He was very happy because the sun was shining. But when he dipped his gourd down in the middle of the maguey plant there was no juice.

"Someone has been here before me," cried Juan. "Someone has taken the sweet juice from the middle of my maguey plant."

Juan looked on the ground all around his maguey plant. He saw some marks on the ground.

"Now I know who took the sweet juice from the middle of my maguey plant," said Juan. "It was that old thief, Señor Coyote."

All day long Juan cut poles with his big knife that is called a machete. He made a point on each end of the pole. Then he put the poles in the ground very close together. They made a fence around his maguey plant. Juan made a little door in the fence close to the ground.

"That door is big enough for Señor Coyote to get to my maguey plant," said Juan to himself. "But when he comes out of this little door I shall hit him with a stick and kill him."

When the moon came over the hills to the East, Juan was waiting in the door of his hut. He was very quiet. And he had put dirt on his clothes so that the Coyote would not smell him and go away.

Juan carried a big stick. He waited and waited in the door of his hut. He was watching the fence that was all around his big maguey plant.

The big moon was going down behind the hills in the West. All night Juan had waited in the door of his hut. He was getting very sleepy.

Then Juan heard Señor Coyote singing to the moon. Señor Coyote was coming nearer and nearer. Señor Coyote came to the big maguey plant. He went around and around the fence. At last he found the door in the fence and went in. He climbed right into the middle of the big maguey and started to drink the sweet juice.

Juan ran to the door in the fence. He raised his big stick and he cried, "Now I have you, Señor Thief."

Señor Coyote was so surprised that he jumped up into the air. In the moonlight Juan could see the Coyote's legs moving as if he

were running in the air. Señor
Coyote looked so funny that Juan
began to laugh.

The Coyote came down to the
ground. He ran around and around
inside the fence. He ran so fast
that he could not find the little
door to get out of the fence.

Señor Coyote looked so funny
that Juan laughed and laughed.
He dropped his stick and held his
sides.

"Ho! Ho! Ho!" laughed Juan. "I
have never seen anything so funny
in my life."

At last Señor Coyote found the
little door in the fence. He went

out of that little door as fast as he could go.

But Juan was laughing so hard that he could not even pick up his big stick.

And so Juan did not kill Señor Coyote that night.

The Son
of Tata Juan

Once upon a time there was a fisherman whose name was Tata Juan. He and his Wife had one little boy named Juanito, which means little John. They lived in a little hut outside of a great city. And they were very poor.

One evening, just as the sun was going down, Juanito ran to his Mother.

"Mother! Mother!" cried Juanito. "A beautiful carriage has just stopped at our door."

The Mother and the Father went to the door of the hut. There was a carriage with six white horses. And a beautiful young woman got out of the carriage. She smiled and said,

"Kind people, let me stay with you tonight."

"You would not like to stay with us, dear lady," said Tata Juan. "We are very poor and our hut has only one room."

"That is all right," said the young woman. "I will spend the night with you. Tomorrow I will go to the city. But I shall return again at night."

Tata Juan and his Wife made the beautiful lady as comfortable as they could. The hut was clean and the beans that the Wife cooked tasted good if you were hungry.

But it was Juanito that the young lady talked to. It was Juanito who brought her cold water from the spring. And it was Juanito who fanned away the flies.

In the morning the carriage with the six white horses stood before the door of the hut. The young lady got into her carriage and went to the city. But in the evening she returned to the hut of Tata Juan.

"I have come for Juanito," said the young lady. "I wish to take him home with me to the town of Canela."

"We cannot let you take our only son," said Tata Juan.

"When we are old, there will be no one to look after us," said the Wife.

"I will look after you," said the young lady. "For I am the Fairy of Canela. Everything that your son wants will be his. And he will not forget his Father and his Mother."

Tata Juan and his Wife did not know what to say to the Fairy. They went outside the hut and sat in the moonlight. They talked together all that night.

In the morning Tata Juan said to the Fairy, "You may take Juanito to Canela with you. You can give our son many things which we can never give him. But do not let him forget his Father and his Mother."

"I thank you for your son," said the Fairy of Canela. "You will never be sorry that you let Juanito go to Canela with me."

The Fairy dressed Juanito in fine clothes. Tata Juan and his Wife did not know from where the fine clothes came. But there stood Juanito looking like a little Prince.

The carriage and the six white horses again stood before the door of the hut. Before the Fairy of Canela got into the carriage, she gave Tata Juan a vase.

"Tata Juan," said the Fairy, "I give you this vase because you and your Wife were kind to me. Whenever you want money, just put your hand in the vase. There will always be money in the vase

for you. And you will never want
for anything."

Then the Fairy of Canela and
Juanito got into the carriage and
away they went.

The Lion, the Ant and the Eagle

Juanito, the son of Tata Juan, was going to live with the Fairy of Canela.

The way to Canela was long. And Juanito got very tired of riding in the beautiful carriage with the six white horses.

"Juanito, do not go to sleep," said the Fairy.

But Juanito was very tired. Slowly, slowly his eyes went shut.

When Juanito opened his eyes he was all by himself. His fine clothes were gone and he had on his old clothes. He could not see the beautiful carriage and the six white horses anywhere.

Juanito called, "Where are you, Fairy of Canela?"

But no one answered.

"I do not know which way to go," said Juanito to himself. "But I will throw my shoe into the air. The way the toe of my shoe points will be the way to go."

Juanito took off his shoe and threw it into the air. And when the shoe fell to the ground, it pointed to the north. And Juanito walked to the north.

The boy had not gone far before he heard a noise. He looked all around.

Juanito saw a Lion and an Ant and an Eagle fighting over a dead cow. The Lion saw the boy and called out,

"Come here, boy. You must help us. What part of the cow shall I eat? What part of the cow shall the Eagle eat? And what part of the cow shall the Ant eat?"

Juanito was afraid of the Lion, and so he said,

"The Ant shall have the head of the cow. The Eagle shall have the legs of the cow. And you,

Señor Lion, shall have the rest of
the cow to eat."

"My boy," said the Lion, "you
have divided the cow for us. And
now I will pay you. Pull out one
of the long hairs in my mane."

Juanito was very much afraid.
But he walked up to the Lion and
pulled a long hair out of his
mane.

"Here," said the Ant. "I will
give you one of my feet."

But the Eagle did not say anything. He just took a leg of the
cow and flew away.

"What shall I do with this hair
and this foot?" asked Juanito.

"Whenever you are in trouble," said the Lion, "hold the hair in your hand and say, 'God and my good Lion.' And if you need the Ant, hold the Ant's foot in your hand and say, 'God and my good Ant'."

"Good," said Juanito. He held the hair from the Lion's mane in his hand and he said, "God and my good Lion."

"What do you want?" asked the Lion.

"I want to go to the town of Canela," said Juanito.

"I will show you the way," said the Lion.

And so Juanito and the Lion and the Ant walked to the North. When the sun went down, they went to sleep under a tree.

In the morning, they heard the Eagle in the tree.

"I will take you to the town of Canela," said the Eagle. "It is a long way and we must have meat. Stay under the tree until a cow comes by. Kill the cow. And then we will have meat for our journey."

The Lion and the Boy and the Ant stayed under the tree. When the sun was high in the sky, a cow came by. The Lion killed the cow. Even after the Eagle, the

Lion, Juanito and the Ant had
eaten all the meat they wanted,
there was much meat left for the
journey to Canela.

"Juanito, get on my back," said
the Eagle. "I will take you to the
town of Canela."

Juanito climbed upon the back
of the Eagle and away they flew.
Seven times the Eagle called for
meat. Seven times Juanito gave
the Eagle a piece of meat. And
now the meat was all gone.

At last the Eagle set Juanito
down by a lake. Juanito was very
tired. He went to sleep beside the
lake.

The Monster

Juanito was sleeping beside the lake. But he did not sleep very long. The Eagle called to him.

"Wake up. Wake up, Juanito. Quickly call the Lion and the Ant. There is a Monster who lives in the lake. He is coming to kill you. The Monster has to be killed before we can get to Canela."

Juanito took the hair that was from the mane of the Lion. He held it in his hand and he said, "God and my good Lion."

Then Juanito held the foot of

the Ant in his hand and said, "God and my good Ant."

There beside the boy stood the Lion and the Ant. And the Lion and the Ant had got there just in time.

Out of the lake came the Monster. He rushed at Juanito. The Monster was going to kill the boy.

But the Ant bit the Monster on the foot. And as the Monster turned his head to see what had hurt his foot, the Lion jumped upon him. There was a great fight. At last the Monster was dead.

"Cut open the Monster," cried the Eagle. And Juanito took his knife and cut open the Monster. A Snake crawled out of the Monster.

"Kill the Snake," cried the Eagle, "and a Dove will fly out of the Snake."

Juanito killed the Snake and a Dove flew up into the air.

At once the Eagle caught the Dove and brought it to Juanito.

"Kill the Dove," cried the Lion. "There is a magic egg inside the Dove. You must have this magic egg to get into the palace of Canela."

Juanito killed the Dove. And inside the Dove he found the magic egg.

"Now," said the Eagle, "we are ready to go to Canela."

"When you get to the palace, a guard will stand at the door," said the Lion. "You must break the magic egg on the guard's head. Then you can go into the palace."

"But if the magic egg is broken before you get to the palace," said the Ant, "we can do nothing more for you."

Juanito climbed upon the back of the Eagle. He carried the magic egg very carefully. And away they flew to Canela.

The Eagle put Juanito down by the door of the palace. And there stood the guard by the door. And the door of the palace was shut.

Juanito took the leg of the Ant and held it in his hand and said, "God and my good Ant."

At once the Ant was there. The Ant bit the guard on the foot. The guard looked down to see what had hurt his foot. Then Juanito ran up to the guard and broke the magic egg upon his head. The door of the palace opened and Juanito walked into the palace.

The Palace
of Canela

Juanito walked through the halls of the palace. He met men and women dressed in beautiful clothes. They all bowed to Juanito. They took him to the room where the King and Queen sat.

The Queen smiled at Juanito. And the King said,

"You have taken a long time to get to our palace."

Then Juanito told the King and the Queen about the Lion and the Ant and the Eagle. He told them about the fight with the Monster. He told them about the magic egg.

"That is a fine story," said the King. But Juanito was so tired that he could hardly keep his eyes open.

The King called his servants and Juanito was given a good supper. Then the servants took the boy to a big room. And in the room was a beautiful soft bed.

Juanito took off his clothes and got into the beautiful soft bed. Juanito had always slept on the ground. He had never slept in a bed.

"I think that this is like being on a soft cloud." said Juanito to himself.

But Juanito could not go to sleep. He was thinking of his Father and of his Mother.

"Juanito, Juanito," called someone under the bed.

"Who are you?" asked Juanito.

"I am the Fairy of Canela. At last you are within the palace of Canela. I have waited a long time for you to get here. And now you will be the King's son and live in the palace."

"But I don't want to be here," said Juanito. "I want to be back home with my own Father and my own Mother. I do not want to live in the palace."

"My little Juanito, I want you to be happy," said the Fairy of Canela. "Tomorrow I will take you back to your Father and your Mother."

In the morning, the carriage with the six white horses stood at the door of the palace. Juanito and the Fairy of Canela got into the carriage.

The King and the Queen were sorry to see Juanito go, for he was a fine boy. But they wanted Juanito to be happy. And so they let the Fairy of Canela take the boy back to his own home.

Many things had happened to Tata Juan and his Wife. Tata Juan had put his hand down in the vase that the Fairy of Canela had given him. He had found money inside the vase. Whenever Tata Juan put his hand inside the vase, he found money.

Now Tata Juan had a fine house in the town. He had a big fishing boat. And every time he took his fishing boat to sea, he came back with many fish.

But the Wife of Tata Juan was

not happy. She kept thinking of
Juanito.

"His eyes were so brown," she
said to Tata Juan. "His lips were
so red. His teeth were so white,
and he was always smiling."

"Yes," said Tata Juan. "Juanito
was a fine boy. And remember, my
good Wife, the Fairy of Canela
said that Juanito would have
everything that he wanted."

One morning when the sun was
just coming up, the Wife of Tata
Juan looked out of her window.
She saw a beautiful carriage and
six white horses in front of the
house.

"Wake up! Wake up! Tata Juan!" called the Wife. "There is a beautiful carriage and six white horses in front of our house."

Tata Juan and his Wife ran out the door of their house. They ran out to the carriage and looked inside. There was Juanito fast asleep in the carriage.

"Our son wanted to come back to his own Father and his own Mother," said Tata Juan.

"And the Fairy of Canela said that Juanito could have anything that he wanted," said the Wife.

Juanito opened his eyes, and got out of the beautiful carriage.

"Father! Mother!" he cried. "But where am I? Where is our hut?"

"We do not live in a hut any longer," said Tata Juan. "We live in a fine house. And there is always money in the vase that the Fairy of Canela gave to me."

Then they heard the Fairy of Canela speak but they could not see her. And they could not see the beautiful carriage and the six white horses.

"Juanito wanted to live with his own Father and his own Mother. I have brought him back to his home. Tata Juan, I will let you keep your big boat and your fine house. But I will take the magic vase back to the palace of Canela. Goodbye, Juanito, you are a fine boy and I will always love you very much."

"Goodbye, Fairy of Canela," called Juanito, "I will always love you. And I am glad that I met the Lion and the Ant and the Eagle. I am glad that the Monster of the Lake was killed. I am glad that I saw your beautiful palace of Canela. But home is best."

The Princess and
the Prince

Long ago there was a King who had a beautiful daughter. One day the King called his daughter to him.

"My child," said the King, "it is time that you were married. I want you to be happy. And so I will let you choose your own husband."

"Thank you, my dear Father," said the Princess. "I am very glad that you will let me choose the man I am to marry."

The Princess looked carefully at every man that came to her Father's palace. When the Princess was carried in her litter through the narrow streets of the town, she looked out through the curtains of the litter. She was always looking for a young man with whom she could fall in love. But the Princess saw no one that she wanted to marry.

The Princess became very sad. "Wait," said the lady-in-waiting. "One day you will see the man you want to marry."

Now it so happened that the young Prince from another

Kingdom over the mountains came to the town where the Princess lived. The Prince came quietly with only a few servants to carry his litter. He did not want the people of the town to know who he was. The King of this country hated the Prince's father.

The young Prince had heard of the wonderful market place in the town on the other side of the mountain. And so he had brought many beautiful things to sell in the market place.

It so happened that on that same day the Princess was carried in a golden litter through the narrow streets of the town.

In one of the narrow streets of the town, the litter in which the Prince was riding met the litter in which the Princess was riding. The street was so narrow that the two litters could not pass.

The Prince got out of his litter and his servants stood aside.

Then the Princess pulled aside the curtains of her litter. She looked right into the face of the Prince. And the Prince looked into the eyes of the Princess.

Not a word was spoken. But

the Princess knew that she had found the man that she could love.

The Prince went back to his own Kingdom. But he could not forget the beautiful girl that he had seen in the litter. He knew that she must be the Princess.

And so the Prince came back to the town where the Princess lived. He had his servants carry his litter past the palace.

The Princess stood in the door-way of the palace. She looked very sad.

The Prince got out of his litter and bowed to the Princess. And suddenly the Princess was happy again.

"I could not forget you," said the Prince. "I came back over the mountains to see you again. I want to marry you and take you to my Father's Kingdom."

"I love you too," said the Princess. "But my Father will not let me marry a man from another Kingdom."

And so the Prince went back to his own country. But he did not forget the Princess. At last he sent a message to the Father of the Princess. He asked the King if he could marry his daughter.

The King was very angry. He called his daughter to him.

"Are you in love with a Prince from another Kingdom?" asked the King.

"Yes," said the Princess. "I love him very much. And he is the only young man that I want to marry."

The King was very, very angry. He sent his daughter to her room. He told the lady-in-waiting that the Princess could not leave her room until she had forgotten all about the Prince from another Kingdom.

The Princess sat in her room
and cried. The lady-in-waiting was
very sorry for her. She was afraid
the Princess would get sick. At last
she sent a message to the Prince.
And the Prince came at night to
the garden of the palace.

The Prince and the Princess
talked together in the garden of
the palace.

"Let us be married and go to
the Kingdom of my Father," said
the Prince.

Many nights the Prince came to
the garden of the palace and talked
with the Princess. One night the
Princess said,

"My Father loves me very much. I am sure he would forgive me if we were married."

The lady-in-waiting helped the Prince and the Princess. And the next night the Prince came with his servants. He took the Princess and the lady-in-waiting away from the palace. And the Prince and the Princess were married.

The next morning the Princess took the Prince to her father.

"Father," said the Princess, "the Prince and I are married. Will you forgive me and love me as you always have?"

The King was very angry but he was sad too.

"You have broken the law of our people," said the King. "You are no longer my daughter."

The Princess hid her face on her husband's shoulder.

"Let all my people hear," cried the King. "No one in my Kingdom can give the Princess and her husband a place to sleep or he will be killed. No one in my Kingdom can give the Princess and her husband any food to eat or he will be killed. That is the law of the Kingdom. The daughter of the King cannot marry a man from another Kingdom."

"Come," said the Prince. "We will go to my Father's Kingdom."

And so the Prince and the Princess started over the mountains. No one would give them a place to sleep. And no one would give them any food to eat.

The Sleeping Lady

The Prince and the Princess went a long, long way over the mountains. At last they came to the Kingdom of the Prince's Father.

The old King was very glad to see his son. But when he found out that his son had married the daughter of the King he hated, he would not let the Princess come into his palace.

"Don't you know," cried the King, "that a Prince of my Kingdom cannot marry a Princess of another Kingdom? It is the law of the country."

"Let all my people hear," cried the King. "No one in my Kingdom can give the Prince and his wife a place to sleep or he will be killed. No one in my Kingdom can give the Prince and his wife any food to eat or he will be killed. That is the law of the Kingdom."

The Prince and the Princess went away into the mountains. They were tired and hungry. They had no home and no servants to care for them. They ate the fruit that they found on the bushes and in the trees.

It was getting very cold in the mountains. At last the Prince and the Princess knew that they must die.

"Tonight is the last night that we will be on this earth," said the Prince. "Tomorrow when the sun comes up over those two high mountains, we will go to meet our gods."

"I know that we will always be together," said the Princess. "The laws of my people wanted to keep us apart. But the laws of the gods are the laws of love. The gods will let us be together."

The next morning when the sun came over the mountains, the

Prince and the Princess prayed to their gods.

Then the Prince said to the Princess,

"The gods have spoken to me. The top of one of the mountains is to be your resting place. The top of the other mountain is to be my resting place. Sleep, dear Princess, on your mountain top. The gods will take care of you. And I, on my mountain top, will keep a fire burning. The burning fire from my mountain top will let all people of the earth know that I love my sleeping Princess. I will watch over her to the end of time."

The Princess climbed to the top of the mountain. When she went to sleep, the gods sent the soft white snow to cover her. And from that day to this there has always been snow on the top of the mountain called Ixtaccihuatl which means Sleeping Lady.

The Prince climbed to the top of the other mountain. And the gods sent fire out of the top of the mountain. And the people on earth knew that the Prince would always be looking at his Princess asleep on the top of the mountain of the Sleeping Lady.

The people on the earth called the Prince's mountain Popocatepetl which means Smoking Mountain.

The people on the earth built a temple for the Princess on the mountain of the Sleeping Lady. And a temple was built on the Smoking Mountain for the Prince.

The Princess is now the goddess Ixtaccihuatl and the Prince is now the god Popocatepetl who looks after the people who live on the mountain side.

Every year the people have two fiestas, one for the Princess and one for the Prince. These fiestas last for two days. There is dancing and many good things to eat. Cookies are made to look like the Princess and the Prince. The cookies are dressed in pretty paper. The people take the cookies to the mountain side. They set up the cookies and put flowers around them. The men build little fires all over the side of The Smoking Mountain.

And when the fiestas are over, I think that the children eat the cookies.

An Eagle
on a Cactus

The city of Mexico was built upon a lake. This is the story of why the Aztecs built their most beautiful city in such a strange place.

The most powerful god of the Aztecs was Huitzilopochtli, who was called the god of war. He was also the god who could make things grow. He was so powerful that Tlaloc, the rain god, would obey him.

The lightning obeyed the war god too. For the Aztecs believed that Huitzilopochtli sent the lightning to kill their enemies.

In the long ago, the Aztecs went from place to place. Wherever they stayed, they built a temple for their war god. In the temple the Aztec priests put the stone statue of Huitzilopochtli. The priests prayed to the statue to tell them what to do. And always the priests told the people.

"The war god tells us to go to the South."

Then the Aztecs would take the statue of their war god and go to the South. They crossed rivers and they climbed mountains. Sometimes they found a beautiful place. The people would build a temple and some houses.

The people would say to the priests,

"Go to the temple and pray to our powerful war god. Ask Huitzilopochtli if we are to build our beautiful city here."

But the priests would say,

"The war god tells us to go to the South. He tells us to build the city where a cactus grows out of a rock."

The Aztecs always did what the

priests of the war god told them to do. They marched to the South.

One evening just as the sun was going down, the Aztecs came to a beautiful lake. They saw something very strange out in the lake.

There was a large rock on an island in the lake. Right out of the rock a cactus plant was growing. An Eagle was sitting on the cactus plant holding a snake in its claws. And the setting sun made the rock and cactus plant and the eagle and the snake look like gold.

"Look! Look! Look!" cried the priests of Huitzilopochtli. "The war god has shown us the place where we are to build our beautiful city."

"But how can we build a city on a little island in a lake?" cried the people.

The priests said, "Huitzilopochtli is strong like the eagle. Huitzilopochtli is wise like the snake. He will tell us how to build our city on the little island in the lake."

The Aztecs began to build their beautiful city on the island in the lake. They made the island bigger and bigger. They built a great high temple to their war god. They also built smaller temples to all the other gods.

The Aztecs built beautiful palaces. They built roads of stone and bridges from their beautiful island to the shores of the lake.

But most wonderful of all, they built gardens on the lake. Large rafts were made of logs. Dirt from the bottom of the lake was piled upon the rafts. Flowers and vegetables and even trees were grown in the dirt upon the rafts in the lake.

The Aztec city on the island in

the lake became the most beautiful city in Mexico. The King of the Aztecs became the most powerful ruler in Mexico.

The Little Slave Girl

There was once a little Aztec Princess who was sold as a slave girl. Her father had died, and her mother had married again. The mother wanted her new husband to have all the land and the riches that the father had left to his little daughter.

One day some men came to the palace. They wanted to buy slaves to take to a Mayan Chief. And the mother sold her daughter to these men.

The little girl grew up in the palace of a Mayan Chief. The Maya people were a kind people. They were good to the little slave girl. And they named her Malinche.

Malinche learned to speak the Mayan language, which was different from the Aztec language. And she learned about the Mayan gods, who were the same as the Aztec gods, but called by other names.

The great god-King called by the Aztecs, Quetzalcoatl, which means Feathered Sky-Snake, was also a Mayan god. It was this god who came down from the sky to be a King to the people. It was he who taught the people on earth to make beautiful things.

In that Mayan palace there was much talk about the god called Quetzalcoatl. For when this god was very old he told his people that he must go away across the sea. But at some time he would send his children back to the people of Mexico. He said his children would be white men with beards.

This was a story that Malinche had heard her own Aztec people tell. And now the Mayan people told the same story. The people in the Chief's palace told Malinche that, in a city to the south by the sea, there were two slaves who were white men with beards. After a bad storm the two white men had come out of the sea. The Mayan Chief of that city had made the two white men his slaves.

One day a messenger from the city by the sea came to the palace where Malinche lived. The messenger told the Mayan Chief that many big houses were out on the sea. The houses-on-the-water had big white wings. And the men in the houses-on-the-water were white men with beards.

One of the two white slaves had

jumped into the sea and swum out to a house-on-the-water. The Chief of the city by the sea sent a messenger in a boat out to the house-on-the-water. The white slave had talked to the messenger and told him that the Chief of the houses-on-the-water wanted gold. He wanted gold to take back to his King across the sea.

The Mayan Chief of the city by the sea sent presents to the Chief of the houses-on-the-water. He told him that if he wanted gold, he was to go north. He told him that to the north was an Aztec city made of gold.

Malinche listened to all of these stories that the messenger told about the white men with beards. She was sure that these were the children of the Aztec god, Quetzalcoatl.

But the Mayan Chief was not so sure that these white men were the children of Quetzalcoatl, the god called the Feathered Sky-Snake. Why would the children of a god want gold for a King who lived across the Sea? The Mayan Chief was afraid these strange men were going to hurt his people.

The Mayan Chief and all his soldiers made ready to fight the white men with beards. They marched to the sea. They wanted to make the white men with beards go back to their King across the sea.

But the white men landed two hundred men with horses and guns and cannon. They were going to fight the Mayan soldiers.

There were ten times as many Mayan soldiers as there were white soldiers. But the Mayan soldiers only had bows and arrows and spears to fight with.

The Mayan soldiers did not know how to fight against the white man's "sticks that spoke with thunder." The Mayan soldiers had never seen horses before. They thought that a man on a horse was a four-legged devil. And the Mayan soldiers did not know how to fight devils.

The white men pushed the Mayan soldiers back to their city. And the white men with beards marched into the city. They did not kill the people of the city. They told the Mayan Chief that all they wanted was gold to take back to their King.

The Chief said,

"Go to the North. Go to the city where the Aztec King,

Montezuma, rules. There you will find a city made of gold."

The white men with beards went back to their houses-on-the-water. They made ready to sail to the North. They wanted to find the city made of gold.

The Mayan Chief wanted to be friends with these strange white men with beards. He sent twenty of his most beautiful slave girls to the chief of the white men. And Malinche was one of those slave girls.

The Chief
of the White Men

Malinche found the house-on-the-water a very strange place. She learned that the white men were not devils. They were very kind to her. The Chief of the white men was called Captain Don Hernando Cortez.

The ten ships under Captain Cortez sailed north for many days. Captain Cortez wanted to find the Aztec city made of gold that the Mayan people had told him was in the North. Malinche learned a little of the Spanish language so that she could talk with the white men with beards.

One day the ship came to a harbor or place where the ships could stop. Men in canoes came out to the ships, and these men spoke a language that only Malinche could understand, for these men were Aztecs.

"Where is your Chief? We want to talk with him," said the Aztecs.

And Malinche pointed to Captain Don Hernando Cortez.

Then began a very strange talk. Captain Cortez spoke the Spanish language. The white man who had been a slave in the Mayan city could speak Spanish and the Mayan language. And Malinche could speak the Mayan language and a little of the Spanish language.

Captain Cortez asked the men in the canoes, "Who are you and from where did you come?"

The white man said to Malinche in the Mayan language, "Who are you and from where did you come?"

And Malinche said to the men in the canoes, in the Aztec language, "Who are you and from where did you come?"

The men in the canoes said, "We are from the great King Montezuma. And we bring presents to the Chief of the white men who lives in the houses-on-the-water."

When Captain Cortez saw the presents made of gold, he knew that the great King, Montezuma, must live in the city made of gold.

Captain Cortez said, "The great King of all who lives across the sea has sent presents to King Montezuma. Go and tell your King that I will visit his city made of gold."

Captain Cortez and his men left the ships in the harbor. They took their cannon and marched to the city of gold. It took them a long time to reach the city of gold, which was built upon a lake. They had to go through thick hot forests. They had to march over mountains.

At last they came to the city on the lake. Cortez and his men thought that it was the most beautiful city that they had ever seen. The city shone in the sunlight as if it was made of gold. And it is true that many of the temples had gold on them.

Montezuma and his nobles came out from the city to meet Captain Cortez and his men. Captain Cortez and King Montezuma talked together with the help of Malinche because Malinche had learned a great deal of Spanish by this time. She could tell Captain Cortez what King Montezuma said, and she could tell King Montezuma what Captain Cortez said.

Malinche told King Montezuma that she was sure that these white men with beards were the children of the god, Quetzalcoatl. She was sure that they had come to help the Mexican people.

Now King Montezuma knew and believed the story about the Aztec god, Quetzalcoatl. He believed that when Quetzalcoatl had gone away, he had told the Aztec people that he would send his children back to Mexico. His children would be white men with beards. So King Montezuma believed that he should help the Captain of the white men in every way.

At first the Aztecs who lived in the city on the lake were kind to Captain Cortez and his men. But some of the men began to steal the gold that was in the temples.

Then one day there was a great dance. Six hundred Aztec men danced before the temple of their war god. Malinche thought it was the most beautiful sight that she had ever seen. But the soldiers did not understand. They thought the Aztecs were going to fight them. So they rushed at the dancers and killed them.

Now the soldiers of King Montezuma were going to drive Captain Cortez and his men out of the city on the lake.

Montezuma tried to tell his soldiers not to fight the white men with beards who were the children of the god Quetzalcoatl. But Montezuma's soldiers killed him. And then they drove Captain Cortez and his men out of the city on the lake.

Many white men were killed. Many, many Aztecs were killed. Most of the beautiful city on the lake was burned. Cortez and what were left of his men had to go back to a friendly city which was nearer the ocean.

History tells us that the next year more and more soldiers came across the sea in the houses-on-the-water with white wings. Captain Cortez and his soldiers went back and took the golden city on the lake. They made the Aztec people their slaves. They sent the gold of the Aztecs to the Spanish King across the water. The Spaniards burned the Aztec temples. They burned the temple to the god Quetzalcoatl.

What happened to Malinche?

Captain Cortez gave her a palace and made her a princess. But Malinche was very sad. The white men with beards had hurt her people. They had burned the temples. They were not the children of the god Quetzalcoatl.

There is a story told in Mexico City about Malinche. Some people say that she cannot rest. She walks the streets of Mexico City, which is built on the same place where the Aztec city stood. Some people even say that on a dark night when there is no moon, they see Malinche crying and crying as she walks the streets of Mexico City. She is crying because she helped the white men with beards make slaves of her people.

How to Say Some
Mexican Words

Divided to show the syllables	How to say the word
Ca-ne-la	Kah-nay-lah
co-yo-te	ki-oh-tay (as Mexicans say it)
fi-es-ta	fee-es-tah
ha-ci-en-da	ah-see-en-dah
Huit-zi-lo-poch-tli	Wee-tsee-loh-poch-tlee
Ix-tac-ci-hua-tl	Ix-tac-see-wah-tl
Juan	hwahn
Juan-i-to	hwahn-ee-toh
ma-che-te	may-shay-tay
mag-uey	mag-way
Ma-lin-che	Mah-lin-shay
Maya	Mah-yah
Quet-zal-co-atl	Ket-sahl-coh-ahtl
Po-po-ca-te-petl	Poh-poh-cah-tay-petl
se-nor	say-nyor
Ta-ta Juan	Tah-tah Hwahn
Tla-loc	Tlay-loc